Primary Dictionary Skills

Ginny Lapage

Collins Primary Dictionary Skills

First published 2001

© HarperCollins*Publishers* Ltd 2001

10 9 8 7 6 5 4 3 2

ISBN 0 00 711990 9

A catalogue record for this book is available from the British Library.

Published by HarperCollins*Publishers* Ltd
77-85 Fulham Palace Road
Hammersmith
London W6 8JB

Telephone ordering and information
0870 0100 441

www.**Collins**Education.com
Online support for schools and colleges

www.**fire**and**water**.com
Visit the book lover's website

Author: Ginny Lapage
Editor: Janet Swarbrick
Cover designer: Susi Martin
Design: Grasshopper Design Company
Illustrator: Juliet Breese

Printed in Great Britain by Martins the Printers, Berwick

Contents

Introduction

Collins Dictionary Skills

Collins Dictionary Skills provide all-in-one support for developing dictionary skills. Each Skills book provides:

- photocopiable activity sheets, differentiated for a wide range of abilities

- clear teaching notes and answers

- lesson planning charts that match each activity to National Literacy Strategy objectives and Scottish 5–14 Guidelines.

For maximum support, use each **Collins Dictionary Skills** book with its matching Collins Children's Dictionary.

Collins Dictionaries – for children aged 2 to 11+

Developed in consultation with teachers, children's lexicographers, educational advisors and literacy, numeracy and science specialists, these clear, colourful dictionaries have been written and designed to support today's Primary classroom requirements.

Collins Children's Dictionaries are carefully streamlined to provide a dictionary for each key level of literacy development. Because Collins' range of dictionaries progressively builds skills, children will be able to move confidently between levels and become independent dictionary users.

Children need to acquire the ability to use a dictionary successfully and independently. Collins Children's Dictionaries have been designed to provide all the support that children need, by means of:

- clear, easy-to-use design

- child-oriented definitions and examples

- progressive building of key skills as children move from level to level.

The Collins Children's Dictionary range:

- *builds essential dictionary skills* progressively, step by step, from beginner to advanced

- supports *today's curriculum needs* from the Early Learning Goals to SATs

- incorporates special features to *encourage independent learning*, such as annotated introductions, theme pages, grammar help, word banks and word histories

- has been *rigorously researched and trialled* with teachers and pupils

- has been compiled by a team of experts.

About *Collins Primary Dictionary*

Collins Primary Dictionary is designed for children aged 8 and over. It is full of helpful and educationally sound features, including:

- **Headwords** and **colour guidewords**, plus an **alphabet line** on every page for easy reference.

- **Other forms** given on the same line as the headword, such as plural nouns, verb tenses or other adjective forms (comparatives and superlatives).

- **Parts of speech** given in full, which identify the headword as a noun, verb, adjective, adverb or pronoun, for example.

- Clear, child-friendly **definitions**. These are **numbered** if there is more than one meaning. Each definition has its own part of speech.

- **Synonyms** and **antonyms** given for some words to extend and vary vocabulary.

- **Word histories** explaining the origins of some words.

- **Examples** in *italics* showing the headword used in context.

- **Pronunciation** help for words where the pronunciation is not obvious, or where there are two ways of pronouncing a word that have different meanings.

- **Related words** are given at the end of some entries, with their part of speech. These identify the noun or adverb form of the word, for example.

- **Alternative spellings** to show spelling variations for headwords and other forms.

- Special **labels**. Some definitions include a label, such as FORMAL, INFORMAL or TRADEMARK, as additional information.

- **Illustrations** and **photos**, where interesting and useful, to provide further information.

- **Usage tips** provide useful information on the spelling and usage of words.

- Where to look for **more information**. Some definitions tell the user to look at another headword or at the pages at the back of the dictionary to find out more.

- **Topic pages**. These support children's writing while helping to build vocabulary. They include **picture pages** with labelled illustrations on topics such as the earth and solar system. **Grammar pages** provide information on parts of speech, punctuation, prepositions, and prefixes and suffixes. **Word banks** and **number banks** provide lists to help children learn and spell difficult words, time words, synonyms and antonyms, abbreviations, measures, numbers and fractions.

About *Collins Primary Dictionary Skills*

Activity sheets

The activity sheets help you to use the *Collins Primary Dictionary* as an active literacy resource. They provide a wide range of activities to help Y4 and Y5 (P3 and P4) children develop basic dictionary skills. They give you, the teacher, a variety of strategies to support literacy objectives.

The activity sheets are also suitable as a focus for class teaching, for use with a small group, or for individual work in class or at home. The range of activities enables you to select appropriate activity sheets to meet the needs of individual children.

The activity sheets are grouped in eight sections:

Using a dictionary
Activity sheets 1 and 2 give children practice in handling an alphabetical list rather than a storybook to be read from cover to cover.

Alphabetical order
Activity sheets 3 to 5 revise activities from Y3 and extend the skills needed for looking up words that begin with the same three letters, and give practice in finding words in the dictionary.

Dictionary organization
Activity sheets 6 to 16 introduce children to the main body of the dictionary and further extend children's skills in using a dictionary confidently. They show how to open a dictionary near the right place and use guide words, and they extend pupils' knowledge of alphabetical order to find the word they are looking for. They also introduce children to the end pages where there are specific lists or collections of information on which to draw.

Definitions
Activity sheets 17 to 22 build on skills taught earlier and encourage children to write their own definitions and dictionary entries.

Spelling
Activity sheets 23 to 31 reinforce spelling strategies by looking at words which share letter strings, compound words, prefixes and suffixes and irregular or unexpected spellings.

Dictionary games and quizzes
Activity sheets 32 to 36 give children the opportunity to have fun while extending their vocabulary and using their dictionaries to check spelling.

Word banks
Activity sheets 37 to 41 provide activities to encourage a broadening vocabulary by collecting and classifying in groups words of special interest to develop class and individual word banks.

Vocabulary extension
Activity sheets 42 to 45 are designed to help pupils use the dictionary to support text level work.

Teacher's notes

The teacher's notes help you by listing the learning objectives, advising on preparation and providing answers to the questions, activity sheet by activity sheet.

Where appropriate, suggestions are given for follow-up work.

The notes end with further ideas for using the *Collins Primary Dictionary* in supporting literacy objectives.

Curriculum planning charts

Time-saving curriculum planning charts are provided for easy reference, to support you when planning your lesson. The National Literacy Strategy chart matches *Collins Primary Dictionary Skills* to word, text and sentence level objectives for Y3, Y4 and Y5. The Scottish 5–14 Guidelines chart matches *Collins Primary Dictionary Skills* to P5 and P6 attainment targets at levels C and D.

Collins Primary Dictionary Skills and the National Literacy Strategy

Activity sheet	NLS objective
Using a dictionary	
1 What is a dictionary? *to use a dictionary*	**Year 4**, Term 1, Word level objective 3
2 Using a dictionary *to use a dictionary*	**Year 4**, Term 1, Word level objective 3
Alphabetical order	
3 Revision of first and second place letters *to organize words alphabetically using the first two letters: consolidation*	**Year 3**, Term 2, Word level objective 23: consolidation
4 Third place letter *to use third place letters to locate and sequence words in alphabetical order*	**Year 4**, Term 1, Word level objective 12
5 Fourth place letter *to use fourth place letters to locate and sequence words in alphabetical order*	**Year 4**, Term 1, Word level objective 12
Dictionary organization	
6 The four quartiles *to know the quartiles of the dictionary: consolidation*	**Year 3**, Term 2, Word level objective 22: consolidation
7 Headwords *to identify parts of speech and select the correct form: consolidation*	**Year 3**, Sentence level work: consolidation
8 Guide words *to have a secure understanding of the purpose and organization of the dictionary: consolidation*	**Year 3**, Term 1 Word level objective 15: consolidation
9 Using the topic pages *to locate additional information provided by a dictionary: consolidation*	**Year 3**, Term 1 Word level objective 15: consolidation
10 Abbreviations and numbers *to use word banks*	**Year 4**, Term 1 Word level objective 3 **Year 4**, Term 2 Word level objective 3 **Year 4**, Term 3 Word level objective 3
11 Words for numeracy *to use word banks*	**Year 4**, Term 1 Word level objective 3 **Year 4**, Term 2 Word level objective 3 **Year 4**, Term 3 Word level objective 3
12 Prefixes and suffixes *to recognize and spell prefixes; to use a range of suffixes*	**Year 4**, Term 2 Word level objective 7 **Year 4**, Term 2 Word level objective 13
13 Synonyms and antonyms *to explore opposites: consolidation and extension;* *to explore synonyms: consolidation and extension;* *to explain the differences between synonyms;* *to investigate further antonyms*	**Year 3**, Term 2, Word level objective 24: consolidation and extension **Year 3**, Term 3, Word level objective 13: consolidation and extension **Year 5**, Term 1, Word level objective 7 **Year 5**, Term 2, Word level objective 10
14 Asking questions *to use question words appropriately: extension*	**Year 3**, Term 1, Sentence level objective 6: extension
15 Prepositions (1) *to identify a range of prepositions; to understand and use the term 'preposition'*	**Year 5**, Term 3, Sentence level objective 3
16 Prepositions (2) *to identify a range of prepositions; to understand and use the term 'preposition'*	**Year 5**, Term 3, Sentence level objective 3

Activity sheet	NLS objective
Definitions	
17 Nouns and verbs *to use the terms 'singular' and 'plural' appropriately: consolidation; to identify basic rules for changing the spelling of nouns when 's' is added: consolidation; to revise work on verbs*	**Year 3**, Term 2, Word level objective 11: consolidation **Year 3**, Term 2, Word level objective 9: consolidation **Year 4**, Term 1, Sentence level objective 2
18 Adjectives and adverbs *to revise work from Y3.2; to use a range of suffixes which can be added to nouns to make adjectives*	**Year 4**, Term 2, Word level objective 13
19 Connectives *to join sentences in more complex ways: consolidation and extension; to recognize how commas, connectives and full stops are used to join and separate clauses*	**Year 3**, Term 3, Sentence level objective 5: consolidation and extension **Year 4**, Term 2, Sentence level objective 4
20 More than one meaning *to understand that some dictionaries provide multiple meanings: consolidation and extension*	**Year 3**, Term 3, Word level objective 15: consolidation and extension
21 Writing definitions *to define familiar vocabulary in their own words (4.1 W11)*	**Year 4**, Term 1, Word level objective 11
22 Defining words *to define familiar vocabulary in their own words and decide whether theirs are as good or better and why*	**Year 4**, Term 1, Word level objective 11
Spelling	
23 Related words *to identify word roots, derivations and spelling patterns*	**Year 5**, Term 1, Word level objective 8
24 Root words *to practise extending and compounding words through adding prefixes and suffixes*	**Year 4**, Term 3, Word level objective 8
25 Word building *to investigate compound words and recognize that they can aid spelling even where pronunciation obscures it*	**Year 4**, Term 3, Word level objective 11
26 Homophones *to distinguish between the spelling and meanings of common homophones*	**Year 4**, Term 1, Word level objective 6
27 Silent letters *to spell and read words with silent letters: extension*	**Year 3**, Term 2, Word level objective 10
28 Spelling tricky words *to use the dictionary to check spellings and proofread*	**Year 4**, Term 3, Word level objective 2
29 When to use apostrophes *to begin to use the apostrophe appropriately in their own writing*	**Year 4**, Term 2, Sentence level objective 2
30 Patterns in spelling (2) *to spell words with common letter strings but different pronunciation*	**Year 4**, Term 3, Word level objective 6
31 Irregular verbs *to spell irregular verb tenses*	**Year 4**, Term 1, Word level objective 8

Activity sheet	NLS objective
Dictionary games and quizzes	
32 Rhyming games *to use rhyme and compose jingles*	**Year 4**, Term 1, Word level objective 13
33 Word search (1) *to use independent spelling strategies*	**Year 4**, Term 1, Word level objective 3 **Year 4**, Term 2, Word level objective 3 **Year 4**, Term 3, Word level objective 3
34 Word search (2) *to use independent spelling strategies*	**Year 4**, Term 1, Word level objective 3 **Year 4**, Term 2, Word level objective 3 **Year 4**, Term 3, Word level objective 3
35 Crossword (1) *to extend vocabulary*	**Year 4**, Term 1, Term 2 and Term 3 Word level objectives
36 Crossword (2) *to extend vocabulary*	**Year 4**, Term 1, Term 2 and Term 3 Word level objectives
Word banks	
37 New words *to collect new words from own reading and from work in other subjects*	**Year 4**, Term 2, Word level objective 37
38 Overused words *to extend vocabulary and build word banks*	**Year 4**, Term 1, Term 2 and Term 3 Word level objectives
39 Topic-based word banks *to extend vocabulary and build word banks*	**Year 4**, Term 1, Term 2 and Term 3 Word level objectives
40 Etymology (1) *to investigate origins and meanings of words*	**Year 4**, Term 3, Word level objective 7
41 Etymology (2) *to investigate origins and meanings of words*	**Year 4**, Term 3, Word level objective 7
Vocabulary extension	
42 Using powerful language (1) *to use alternative words and expressions which are more accurate or interesting than the common choices*	**Year 4**, Term 2, Word level objective 9
43 Using powerful language (2) *to extend common vocabulary for ways of introducing and concluding dialogue: revision and extension*	**Year 3**, Term 1, Word level objective 19: revision and extension
44 Creating exciting texts *to develop use of settings in own writing, making use of work on adjectives and figurative language to describe settings effectively*	**Year 4**, Term 2, Text level objective 10
45 Creating exciting texts *to write a non-chronological report, including some of the organizational devices*	**Year 4**, Term 1, Text level objective 27

Collins Primary Dictionary Skills and the Scottish 5–14 Guidelines

P5/6 attainment targets at Level C/D

Activity sheet number

	1	2	3	4	5	6	7	8	9	10	11	12	13	14	15	16	17	18	19	20	21	22	23	24	25	26	27	28	29	30	31	32	33	34	35	36	37	38	39	40	41	42	43	44	45
Reading for information																																													
Locating specific information									✓	✓	✓																					✓	✓											
Using a dictionary		✓	✓	✓	✓	✓	✓													✓	✓														✓	✓	✓	✓	✓	✓	✓				
Alphabetical order		✓	✓	✓		✓																																							
Locating and sequencing words			✓	✓	✓																																								
Matching meaning with context													✓	✓	✓	✓	✓	✓	✓																		✓								
Awareness of genre																																													
Understanding how a dictionary is organized		✓	✓			✓	✓	✓	✓	✓	✓																																		
Functional writing																																													
Writing definitions of words		✓						✓		✓										✓	✓	✓																							
Using words in sentences										✓			✓	✓	✓	✓	✓			✓										✓	✓							✓	✓	✓	✓	✓	✓		
Selecting facts/emphasizing key ideas																																													✓
Spelling																																													
Spelling strategies																												✓				✓	✓												
Spelling rules			✓																					✓		✓		✓	✓																
Spelling patterns																								✓	✓	✓	✓				✓														
Prefixes and suffixes										✓														✓				✓	✓																
Knowledge about language														✓	✓	✓		✓	✓	✓					✓	✓			✓																
Imaginative writing																								✓																		✓			
Punctuation and structure																																											✓		

Collins Primary Dictionary Skills
Activity Sheets

Using a dictionary

1 What is a dictionary?
to use a dictionary

2 Using a dictionary
to use a dictionary

Alphabetical order

3 Revision of first and second place letters
to organize words alphabetically using the first two letters: consolidation

4 Third place letter
to use third place letters to locate and sequence words in alphabetical order

5 Fourth place letter
to use third and fourth place letters to locate and sequence words in alphabetical order

Dictionary organization

6 The four quartiles
to know the quartiles of the dictionary: consolidation

7 Headwords
to identify parts of speech and select the correct form: consolidation

8 Guide words
to have a secure understanding of the purpose and organization of the dictionary: consolidation

9 Using the topic pages
to locate additional information provided by a dictionary: consolidation

10 Abbreviations and numbers
to use word banks

11 Words for numeracy
to use word banks

12 Prefixes and suffixes
to recognize and spell prefixes; to use a range of suffixes

13 Synonyms and antonyms
to explore opposites and synonyms: consolidation and extension; to explain the differences between synonyms; to investigate further antonyms

14 Asking questions
to use question words appropriately: extension

15 Prepositions (1)
to identify a range of prepositions; to understand and use the term 'preposition'

16 Prepositions (2)
to identify a range of prepositions; to understand and use the term 'preposition'

Definitions

17 Nouns and verbs
to use the terms 'singular' and 'plural' appropriately: consolidation; to identify basic rules for changing the spelling of nouns when 's' is added: consolidation; to revise work on verbs

18 Adjectives and adverbs
to use a range of suffixes which can be added to nouns to make adjectives

19 Connectives
to join sentences in more complex ways: consolidation and extension; to recognize how commas, connectives and full stops are used to join and separate clauses

20 More than one meaning
to understand that some dictionaries provide multiple meanings: consolidation and extension

21 Writing definitions
to define familiar vocabulary in their own words

22 Defining words
to define familiar vocabulary in their own words and decide whether theirs are as good or better and why

Spelling

23 Related words
to identify word roots, derivations and spelling patterns

24 Root words
to practise extending and compounding words through adding prefixes and suffixes

25 Word building
to investigate compound words and recognize that they can aid spelling even where pronunciation obscures it

26 Homophones
to distinguish between the spelling and meanings of common homophones

27 Silent letters
to spell and read words with silent letters: extension

28 Spelling tricky words
to use the dictionary to check spellings and proofread

29 When to use apostrophes
to begin to use the apostrophe appropriately in their own writing

30 Patterns in spelling
to spell words with common letter strings but different pronunciation

31 Irregular verbs
to spell irregular verb tenses

Dictionary games and quizzes

32 Rhyming games
to use rhyme and compose jingles

33 Word search (1)
to use independent spelling strategies

34 Word search (2)
to use independent spelling strategies

35 Crossword (1)
to extend vocabulary

36 Crossword (2)
to extend vocabulary

Word banks

37 New words
to collect new words from own reading and from work in other subjects

38 Overused words
to extend vocabulary and build word banks

39 Topic-based word banks
to extend vocabulary and build word banks

40 Etymology (1)
to investigate origins and meanings of words

41 Etymology (2)
to investigate origins and meanings of words

Vocabulary extension

42 Using powerful language (1)
to use alternative words and expressions which are more accurate or interesting than the common choices

43 Using powerful language (2)
to extend common vocabulary for ways of introducing and concluding dialogue: revision and extension

44 Creating exciting texts
to develop use of settings in own writing, making use of work on adjectives and figurative language to describe settings effectively

45 Creating interesting texts
to write a non-chronological report, including some of the organizational devices

Teacher's notes

Using a dictionary

What is a dictionary?

Learning objective: *to use a dictionary*

Before you start
- Using examples of different types of reference books, explain they are arranged alphabetically to make it easy to find words, names and information.
- Elicit what the children already know about the purpose and organization of a dictionary. Flick through the dictionary to confirm or elaborate that it helps us check spellings, lists words alphabetically and gives their definitions.

Answers
1. and 2. Check that the children's answers are correct.   3. c h q u x
4. *(left to right)* behk; adhk; abep; mopw; alno; anpq   5. a; zucchini
6. *(left to right)* gadget; pace; each; I; tab; macaroni
7. *(left to right)* kosher; wrung; lyrics; rye; Qur'an; byte

More to do
- Discuss the strategies the children used to look up the words for questions 6 and 7. Show how the alphabet line at the side of the page and the guide words at the top of the page can help them.

Using a dictionary

Learning objective: *to use a dictionary*

Before you start
- Discuss the "Using this dictionary" pages at the beginning of the dictionary.
- Show the children the parts of the dictionary discussed and demonstrate how it can be used.
- For question 1, pairs of children will need a means of timing each other.

Answers
2. believe; people; mirror   3. a notebook with a separate space or page for each day of the year (in children's own words)   4. *(left to right)* noun; verb; adjective; adverb; pronoun; preposition   5. a word that means the opposite of another word   6. in the topic pages at the back of the dictionary.

More to do
- Ask the children to make up a question for the class to answer, making sure they know where and what the answer is themselves.

Alphabetical order

Revision of first and second place letters

☐ **Learning objective:** *to organize words alphabetically using the first two letters: consolidation*

 Before you start

- Have a simple alphabet quiz, for example ask the children which letter comes before or after another letter.

 Answers

1. checkout evil insect laundry mound quarter severe; antelope draught nice orange tractor unique wooden; balloon fragment hurricane plastic reason value yellow   **2.** caveman Christmas clinic conservatory crack current; saucer scramble secret sorcerer special squash; petal physics pincers pleasant policy precious   **3.** and **4.** Check that the children's answers are correct.

Activity 4 — Third place letter

☐ **Learning objective:** *to use third place letters to locate and sequence words in alphabetical order*

 Before you start

- Revise finding words by their first then their second letters as a class activity. Demonstrate identifying the third letter of a word. Play a short game to find several words by their third letter for example: *dappled dare dash*; *lagoon laptop laser*; *policy pompous poverty*.

 Answers

1. adapt adequate admission adopt advice; dial dimple dirty disk dive; snap sneak snivel snow snuggle; laboratory lagoon land larva late
2. *(left to right)* fake; evict; pouch; gas; deed; trod   **3.** *(left to right)* thrust; holy; diplomatic; security; white; vocabulary   **4.** *(left to right)* telly rhinoceros sherry flaunt transport diagonal

 More to do

- Ask the children in pairs to devise their own tasks using third letter place order. Each child selects five words from the dictionary which have the same first two letters but a different third letter. They ask their partner to put them in alphabetical order. They use the dictionary to check their answers.

Activity 5 — Fourth place letter

☐ *Learning objective: to use third and fourth place letters to locate and sequence words in alphabetical order*

Before you start
● Revise sorting selections of words with the same first three letters into alphabetical order with the class.

 Answers
1. discount dishonest display disregard dissolve; notebook nothing noticeable notorious; speak speckled speechless spell spend; wheat wheelbarrow when wherever whether   2. Check that the children's answers are correct.
3. *(left to right)* famished, fan; curl, currency; whale, what; building, bulge; van, vanilla; idiotic, idol

 More to do
● In pairs, the children take turns to select five words from the dictionary that have the same first three letters but a different fourth letter and ask their partner to put them in alphabetical order. They use the dictionary to check their answers.

Dictionary organization

Activity 6 — The four quartiles

☐ *Learning objective: to know the quartiles of the dictionary: consolidation*

 Before you start
● Demonstrate how you can open the dictionary near a word you want to find, by thinking of the dictionary as divided into four sections.
● Ask the children to open the dictionary in the first, second, third and end section, each time writing down the letters they find in the section.
● Write the letters for the four quartiles on the board and ask children to suggest words that belong in each one.

 Answers
1. clean, balloon, disturb; imitate, meridian, June; ox, projector, quarrel; weld, savings, trout; balloon clean disturb imitate June meridian ox projector quarrel savings trout weld   2. f–m, n–r, s–z, s–z, n–r, f–m, f–m, a–e; 1, 3, 2, 2; dance fiend grab imam never roller-skate swim verb

 More to do
● In pairs, children practise opening the dictionary near to a suggested word and time how long it takes to find the word. Suggest using the outside edge of the dictionary to help, as that will give an indication of the quartiles.

Activity 7 — Headwords

☐ *Learning objective: to identify parts of speech and select the correct form: consolidation*

 Before you start

- Revise earlier work on parts of speech: nouns, adjectives, verbs, adverbs, pronouns, prepositions and pronouns.

- Write a list of words on the board and ask the children to identify the part of speech.

- Put some of these words into sentences showing how other forms are used in different contexts.

 Answers

1. monsters, prompted, tackling, shakiest, littered, flans, foxes, getting, oozed, scratches, grown   2. *(left to right)* verb, noun, adjective, conjunction, pronoun, adverb, preposition or adverb, adjective, adverb

Activity 8 — Guide words

☐ *Learning objective: to have a secure understanding of the purpose and organization of the dictionary: consolidation*

 Before you start

- Show the position of the guide words at the tops of the pages (the left hand giving the first word on that page and the right hand giving the last word on that page).

- Demonstrate locating the appropriate pages for a word by finding the two guide words that the sought word comes between.

- Go through the process: identify the first letter of the word; open the book at the correct quartile; select the pages between the appropriate guide words; look at second, third, fourth letter order if appropriate; find the headword.

 Answers

1. card, castle; deer, demolish; Internet, investigation; udder, uneven; rabbi, ram; light, lit; ooze, orienteering; rewarding, ritual; suppress, swept
2. The children should write their own definitions. Here are some suggestions: a long, narrow piece of high land; a large brass musical instrument that can produce very low notes; a type of grain; a small shellfish with a pointed shell that attaches itself very firmly to rocks; weak or fragile; someone who writes music.

Activity 9

Using the topic pages

☐ *Learning objective:* to locate additional information provided by a dictionary: consolidation

Before you start

● Locate the topic pages at the back of the dictionary and discuss what topics or points are included.

Answers

1. Atlantic 2. northern 3. miniature 4. km 5. V
6. equilateral, isosceles 7. Mercury, Pluto
8. French, Spanish, Italian, Greek, Latin, Hindi

More to do

● Groups of children can form teams and set each other a quiz based on the information in the topic pages.

Activity 10

Abbreviations and numbers

☐ *Learning objective:* to use word banks

Before you start

● Discuss using abbreviations. Gather some suggestions and write them on the board. Look them up on page 6 or in the main body of *Collins Primary Dictionary* to see if they are there and what they mean. Explain that not all dictionaries have every word you can think of.

● Talk about Roman numerals and what the letters stand for.

● Remind the children that words can be represented by letters, short forms or numbers.

Answers

1. please turn over; television; millilitre; digital video/versatile disc; anonymous 2. CL; LXII; VIII; LXXXIX; CLXVII; MMIV 3. 2; 9; 159; 6; 500; 4
4. tricycle, a three wheeled cycle; biplane, an aeroplane with two pairs of wings; solo, one person singing; twins, two babies born at the same time; duel, a fight between two people; unicorn, an animal from mythology with one horn; century, a period of one hundred years; octogenarian, someone who is eighty years old; centipede, a creature with one hundred feet; trio, three people singing together;

More to do

● Ask the children to look up other words in the dictionary that start with *bi*, *tri* and *octo* to show that *bi* means *two*, *tri* means *three*, and *octo*, *eight*.

Activity 11

Words for numeracy

 Learning objective: *to use word banks*

 Before you start

- Talk about recording numbers as words and as digits. Demonstrate on the flip chart or board. First, use numbers with units only, then with tens and units only, and lastly with hundreds, tens and units.

 Answers

1. *(left to right)* sixty; seventeen; forty-two; ninety; one hundred and six; one thousand; ten thousand and two; ten thousand one hundred; one million
2. *(left to right)* eighth; first; twenty-first; third; twentieth; fifteenth
3. cuboid; quadrilateral; sphere   4. a written symbol; a smaller amount; a straight line that slopes from one corner of a shape to another; the outer line or edge of a circle; one of the two sides of a graph; a set of numbers or letters set out in rows and columns; the amount out of a hundred (%); the number of times one number can be divided into another; an angle of 90°

 More to do

- Collect words which are used specially for numeracy. Build up a word bank.

Activity 12

Prefixes and suffixes

Learning objectives: *to recognize and spell prefixes; to use a range of suffixes*

Before you start

- Write root words, prefixes and suffixes on the white board or blackboard.
- Show the children how to build up words by adding prefixes and suffixes and talk about how the meanings change.

 Answers

1. underground; mistrust; submerge; reappear; prehistoric; telephone
2. *(left to right)* swimmer; helpful; childhood; snapped; kingdom; cracking/cracker/cracked; sadder/saddest; truthful; artist; dangerous; attendant/attended/attending; lighter/lightest/lighting

 More to do

- The children can build up word banks of prefixes and suffixes.

Activity 13
Synonyms and antonyms

Learning objectives: to explore opposites: consolidation and extension; to explore synonyms: consolidation and extension; to explain the differences between synonyms; to investigate further antonyms

Before you start
- Talk about words with similar meanings (synonyms) and those with opposite meanings (antonyms).
- In the dictionary, show children the entries for antonyms and synonyms both as part of the headword entry and in the topic pages.

Answers
1. connect/link/fasten/tie; engine; confirm/verify; headstrong; extremely
2. *analogue* . . . not so easy . . . was shown by pointers; *informal* . . . casual clothes; *light* . . . could see . . . so did not fall . . .; *wrong* . . . cannot have . . .; *more* . . . not have to hurry

More to do
- In pairs, the children play Same or Different. They take turns to select pairs of words from the dictionary which have antonyms (different meanings) or synonyms (same meanings) given and ask their partner "Same or Different?"

Activity 14
Asking questions

Learning objective: to use question words appropriately: extension

Before you start
- Discuss how questions are shown in writing (with a question mark).
- Discuss how you know a question is being asked when people are talking.
- Give statements and ask the children to turn them into questions by using a question word such as *who, whose, what, why, when, where, which* or *how.*

Answers
1. Why was play cancelled? Where was the ball? Who did that? Who has the longest hair in class? What are you doing? How do I word process my work?
2. What was growing in Mr Jones' window box? Why were weeds growing in . . .? When were weeds growing in . . .? Where were weeds growing? Which weeds were growing in . . .? How were weeds growing in . . .? In whose window box were weeds growing?

More to do
- In groups, the children have a conversation where every question is answered by another question. If they answer with a statement, they are out. The winner is the last child left.

Activity 15

Prepositions (1)

 Learning objectives: *to identify a range of prepositions; to understand and use the term 'preposition'*

Before you start
- Talk about how prepositions are placed before a noun or pronoun and that they describe place, movement and time.
- With the class, look at the section in the dictionary on prepositions (pages 438–9).

Answers
across/over; under/by/through; under/beneath; against; until; by/near/beside; beside; around; for; upon/on; in; between

More to do
- Write prepositions on the flip chart or board. Read out or write a sentence omitting the preposition. An appropriate word should be selected by the class or by the children in turn.

Activity 16

Prepositions (2)

 Learning objectives: *to identify a range of prepositions; to understand and use the term 'preposition'*

Before you start
- Revise previous work on prepositions and look again at the section in the dictionary on prepositions (pages 438–9).

Answers
through; behind; before; towards; along; between; over; under; through; over; in

More to do
- Share the children's responses. Are there alternatives? Could more than one preposition be used? Which is more effective?

Definitions

Nouns and verbs

 Learning objectives: *to use the terms 'singular' and 'plural' appropriately: consolidation; to identify basic rules for changing the spelling of nouns when 's' is added: consolidation; to revise work on verbs*

 Before you start

- Identify nouns and verbs in a selection of sentences on the flip chart or board.

- Identify singular and plural nouns.

- Show how the dictionary helps with the spelling of the different forms of the words.

 Answers

1. *(left to right)* potatoes; armies; geese; pianos; valleys; wolves; women; roofs; children   **2.** The *Britannia* was due to dock in Bristol at noon. Hundreds of people had gathered to see her sail up the River Avon. They had banners and flags to welcome her. It was a bright day, although a little cloudy. Suddenly, a murmur ran through the crowd. A dark shape began to form in the distance. Soon they could see the ship with the crew lined up to wave back at them. Madge, Ida and I cheered along with the rest.
3. argued; will win; gone; fell; dreaming

 More to do

- Each child can choose a few sentences from a reading book to copy out, and identify the nouns and verbs by underlining with two different colours.

Activity 18   Adjectives and adverbs

Learning objective: *to use a range of suffixes which can be added to nouns to make adjectives*

Before you start

- Talk about using adjectives and adverbs to make writing more interesting. Show how the dictionary helps with the spelling of these words in their different forms.

Answers

1. tall, huge; pink, delicate; hot, humid; lost, old; seven, three
2. soon; anxiously; terribly; soundly; slowly   3. Check the children have chosen appropriate words such as: quietly, long, soundly; silently, old; swiftly, ancient; bad-tempered, angrily, naughty; tall, repeatedly, wooden

More to do

- Play the Adverb Game: one child goes out of sight and sound of the others who decide on the manner in which they are going to do something, for example happily or slowly. The child returns and says what action (verb) they are to do, for example walk or sing. The individual has to guess the adverb demonstrated, for example walking *sadly*.

Activity 19   Connectives

Learning objectives: *to join sentences in more complex ways: consolidation and extension; to recognize how commas, connectives and full stops are used to join and separate clauses*

Before you start

- Divide the class into three groups. Group one thinks of a sentence, group two thinks of another sentence that is linked to it, group three provides the connecting word or phrase.
- Talk about linking sentences to make them more interesting. Remind the children that there are word banks at the back of the dictionary to help them.

Answers

1. until; whenever; before; as; while; because; although
2. then; but/nevertheless; now; for instance/for example; and meanwhile; and/however

More to do

- Share the children's responses. Are there alternatives? Which is most effective?

Activity 20 More than one meaning

Learning objective: *to understand that some dictionaries provide multiple meanings: consolidation and extension*

Before you start
- Ask the children how many meanings they can think of for *bank* (for example a place to keep money, a grassy bank, to rely on something). Tell the children that words can have more than one meaning and that dictionaries can help them find out what they are.

Answers
1. hoard 2; mangle 2; tackle 3; will 4

   The children should write sentences to demonstrate one meaning of *mangle*, *tackle* and *will*.

2. The children should write sentences for two different meanings of the words *rumble*, *narrow*, *present* and *font*.

More to do
- Play Call My Bluff. Have three definitions (one true and two false) for one word written on separate cards. The children guess which is the correct one.

Activity 21 Writing definitions

Learning objective: *to define familiar vocabulary in their own words*

Before you start
- Talk about the importance of accurate definitions. The definition should help a reader to understand the meaning of the word.
- Try brainstorming some definitions orally.

Answers
- The answers will depend on the children. Check whether their definitions are correct.

More to do
- The children check how close each of their definitions is to that in the dictionary and discuss whether theirs are as good and if not, why.

Activity 22 — Defining words

 Before you start
- The children practise giving accurate oral definitions for others to work out what the word is.

 Answers
- The children can check their definitions in the dictionary but should write the definitions in their own words.

More to do
- The children check how close their definitions are to those in the dictionary and discuss whether theirs are as good or better and why.

Spelling

Activity 23 — Related words

 Before you start
- Talk about noticing related words in a dictionary.
- Look up *reality* and see what headwords are listed before and after it (real, realistic, reality, realize, really). Ask how the headwords are related (the root word is *real*).
- If the children need help with question 2 on the activity sheet, explain that in Latin *magnus* means *great* and *pedis* means *foot*.

 Answers
1. caveman, cavity; microwave, microscope; icicle, ice cream; detective, detector; pacifist, Pacific   2. make bigger/ be great in appearance or behaviour, big/great; a lever or bike pedal you push with your feet/someone who is walking, using feet

 More to do
- The children look for more words that are linked in the dictionary. They could be grouped to look at specific letters of the alphabet, and could begin to collect examples of word families in their personal words banks or a class word bank.

Activity 24 · Root words

Learning objective: *to practise extending and compounding words through adding prefixes and suffixes*

 Before you start
- Talk about the root of a word being the part you are left with when you take away any prefixes or suffixes.

 Answers
1. dis-, obey, -ient; dis-, satisfy, -ed; under-, estimate, -ed; un-, like, -ly; pre-, mature, ly; ir-, resist, -ible
2. any correctly spelt variants with appropriate root words are acceptable

 More to do
- Ask the children to check their spellings in the dictionary.
- Discuss that some spellings of the root words had to change when they had suffixes added or taken away.

Activity 25 · Word building

Learning objective: *to investigate compound words and recognize that they can aid spelling even where pronunciation obscures it*

 Before you start
- Gather some compound words (made from two smaller words put together) from the class such as *rainbow* or *buttercup* as examples.
- Talk about how endings added to words can change their part of speech, for example *colour* is a noun. When you add *-ful* to make *colourful*, it becomes an adjective.
- Revise nouns, adjectives and adverbs, and tell the children they can find help on parts of speech at the back of the dictionary.

 Answers
1. *(left to right)* toothache/headache; postoffice/postman; snowdrop/ snowboard/snowball; overground/underground; headlight/spotlight; lifeboat/lifeline; snowdrop/raindrop; moonlight/moonbeam; afternoon; football/footbridge; headboard/skateboard/snowboard (other variants that form correct compound words are acceptable) 2. *(left to right)* wealth; thought; imagination; sight; operation; attraction; cruelty; collection; friend/friendship; breath 3. *(left to right)* childlike; fifth, silky; stormy; favourable/favourite; carefree/careful; dangerous; peaceful; sunny
4. happily; truly; horribly; sweetly; heavily; noisily.

Activity 26 — Homophones

> **Learning objective:** *to distinguish between the spelling and meanings of common homophones*

Before you start
- Talk about words which sound the same but which have different meanings and different spellings.
- Tell the children that they can find help with homonyms at the back of the dictionary.

Answers
1. *(left to right)* buoy; quay; whale; doe; ruff; shore
2. Check that the children's sentences demonstrate the correct usage of the words given.
3. bored; principal; hire; groan; Their, floor; holy, place; sale, dear, buy

More to do
- Share a selection of responses from the children. Ask for comments and examples of other ways of using a particular word.

Activity 27 — Silent letters

> **Learning objective:** *to spell and read words with silent letters: extension*

Before you start
- Say some words with silent letters and ask children to spell the words for you to write on the flip chart or board. If they miss a letter, leave a gap and return to it. Remind them that some words have letters you cannot hear when the word is spoken.

Answers
1. *(left to right)* t, b, g, h, h, h, w, b, k, n, gh, n, c, c, b, gh   2. eighteen, exhaust, scissors, rhythm, Wednesday   3. bomb, doubt, crumb, climb; knight, knot, knit, knee; wreck, wrap, write, sword

More to do
- Ask the children to think of some ways to help to remember the silent letters. You might sound the silent letters in your head when you say the word to yourself.

Activity 28 Spelling tricky words

Learning objective: *to use the dictionary to check spellings and proofread*

Before you start
- Talk about spelling words that are difficult. Choose three or four from the "Tricky words to spell" list at the back of the dictionary, for example *February, hiccup, awful.* Ask the children to attempt to spell them. Agree with them that it is difficult as they are not always written as they sound. Some words have to be remembered in a special way such as by using a mnemonic: *It is only really **necessary** to have one collar and two socks but to be really **successful** you need two collars and two socks.*

Answers
jewellery; catastrophe; guard (2); despair; embarrassed; arguing; neighbour; tomatoes; library; imaginary; gardener; mysterious; balloon; camouflage; seized; ridiculous

More to do
- Children prepare one or two sentences for careful proofreading and checking by their partner and include one tricky word in each.

Activity 29 When to use apostrophes

Learning objective: *to begin to use the apostrophe appropriately in their own writing*

Before you start
- Talk about homophones, in particular those that have apostrophes. Ask the children to suggest words that sound alike but have different meanings.
- Talk about the rules for using apostrophes to show possession in singular nouns: *the man's hat*, and in plural nouns: *the doctors' surgeries.*
- Talk about contractions or short forms and make lists showing the word in full and contracted using an apostrophe.

Answers
1. she's; it's; they're   2. They're, there; their; it's; There's; it's; He's

More to do
- Make flash cards of the homophones on activity sheet 29. The children take turns in saying a sentence containing one of the words taught and a child holds up the appropriate card.

Activity 30

Patterns in spelling

Learning objective: *to spell words with common letter strings but different pronunciation*

Before you start
- Read through the words in the list (*rough, cough, trough, plough, dough, through*) and draw attention to the common letter string. Discuss the pronunciation and meanings of the words.

Answers
1. *(left to right)* oo, choose; ou, route; ove, move; ear, heard; ork, work; ead, bead; eat, great; eight, height   2. Check that the children have written sentences that demonstrate their understanding of each spelling pattern.

More to do
- Ask the children to each choose a sentence to read out.

Activity 31

Irregular verbs

Learning objective: *to spell irregular verb tenses*

Before you start
- Talk about verbs in general and the patterns they follow.

- Draw attention to the verb forms given in full in the dictionary.

- Explain the past, present and future tenses with examples on the board.

- Then introduce the verbs on activity sheet 31 and explain that they do not follow the usual, or regular, patterns of spelling. Explain that these are called irregular verbs.

Answers
1. *(left to right)* coming/going, went, am, do, are, having, does/did, doing, being   2. said; ate; knew; brought; chose; wrote; frozen; kept

Dictionary games and quizzes

Rhyming games

 Before you start

- Talk about rhymes and rhyming patterns. Ask the children what rhymes they know and what TV jingles they remember.
- Remind them that when two words rhyme, both words have a very similar sound.

 Answers

1. grand, hand, land, sand etc; dip, grip, lip, ship etc; date, mate, slate, state etc; bake, cake, fake, rake etc 2. born, corn, faun, forlorn etc; bear, care, mare, pear etc; core, four, more, your etc 3. chair, pear, half

More to do

- Ask the children to write a jingle for a radio programme or an advertising poster.
- The children then read out their jingles.

Activity 33 Word search (1)

 Before you start

- Tell the children that all the words in the word search grid can be found under "Tricky words to spell" (page 435).
- Make sure the children know how a word search works.

 Answers

balloon
beautiful
diesel
develop
hiccup
jealous
library
parallel
people
quiet
ridiculous
twelfth

Y	R	P	M	X	J	E	A	L	O	U	S
H	I	C	C	U	P	X	D	M	P	P	B
T	D	I	E	S	E	L	E	T	F	E	A
L	I	B	R	A	R	Y	V	W	M	O	L
W	C	X	V	C	K	I	E	E	O	P	L
L	U	R	P	A	R	A	L	L	E	L	O
B	L	C	D	E	S	T	O	F	E	E	O
N	O	Q	W	G	H	I	P	T	B	F	N
Q	U	I	E	T	A	J	O	H	O	D	O
A	S	B	E	A	U	T	I	F	U	L	C

Activity 34 — Word search (2)

☐ *Learning objective:* to use independent spelling strategies

Before you start
- Tell the children that all the words in the word search grid can be found under "Time" (page 444).
- Make sure the children know how a word search works.

Answers

aeon
duration
elapse
eternity
frequently
immemorial
never
rarely
soon
span
spring
twice

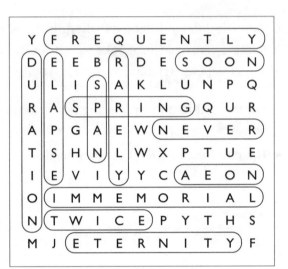

Activity 35 — Crossword (1)

☐ *Learning objective:* to extend vocabulary

Before you start
- Tell the children that all these words can be found in the A to Z section of the dictionary.

Answers

Across: 1. skip 3. May 4. sculpture 5. cave 6. mean 8. sting

Down: 2. illness 3. mauve 4. sock 7. no

Crossword (2)

☐ *Learning objective: to extend vocabulary*

Before you start

● Tell the children that these words can be found in the A–Z section of the dictionary, except for 4 Across, which can be found at the beginning of the dictionary under "Abbreviations".

Answers

Across: 1. mayor 4. e.g. 5. chef 7. if 8. eel 9. frizzy
Down: 1. mischief 2. yodel 3. red 6. relay

Word banks

New words

☐ *Learning objective: to collect new words from own reading and from work in other subjects*

Before you start

● Talk about what you do when you come across a word you do not know.

● Gather strategies from the children for learning new words and using them in written and oral work.

Answers

Check that the children's definitions are correct.

More to do

● Discuss the words the children found and ask for suggestions for usage.

Activity 38

Overused words

☐ *Learning objective:* to extend vocabulary and build word banks

 Before you start

- Talk about what makes a story exciting. Discuss words that are overused such as *like* and *big*.

- Ask the children to suggest alternatives.

- Use the dictionary to help think of other words that could be used instead.

- Start a class word bank to collect alternatives.

 Answers

Check that the children's sentences use the synonyms correctly.

 More to do

- Compare the children's lists and discuss the best alternatives. Make a class word bank wall poster which can be added to as children find more exciting vocabulary.

Activity 39

Topic-based word banks

☐ *Learning objective:* to extend vocabulary and build word banks

 Before you start

- Ask the children to tell you what they think the environment is, then as a class, look for the definition of *environment* in the dictionary.

- Discuss why the children think it is important to look after the environment.

- Look for the definition of *energy* in the dictionary and discuss with the children what we need energy for.

- Explain that the children should check in their dictionary and then write their definition for each word on activity sheet 39 in their own words. They will be building their own individual word banks.

 Answers

Check that the children's definitions are correct and written in their own words.

More to do

- Ask the children to write some sentences using the words they have defined to explain why they think it is important to look after the environment and to explain what we need energy for.

Activity 40 Etymology (1)

☐ *Learning objective: to investigate origins and meanings of words*

Before you start
- Explain that etymology is the study of word origins. Talk about settlers and invaders all over the world, about travel and many cultures living together. Discuss how our language is very special and always growing and changing. Can the children think of any words that may have come from another language, for example *spaghetti* from Italian?

Answers
1. *(left to right)* Latin; Hindi; French; Hindi; Greek; Old English; Greek; Latin
2. Latin, *manus*, hand; Anglo-Saxon, war, *Tiw* (said *tue*); Persian, leg clothing; French, present yourselves!; Romani, red, *pobbel* 3. Check that the children's sentences use their chosen words correctly.

More to do
- Ask the children to look through the dictionary and find five other words which come from another language. They can share some of their findings.

Activity 41 Etymology (2)

☐ *Learning objective: to investigate origins and meanings of words*

Before you start
- Ask the children what they understand the word "etymology" to mean, as a short revision of activity sheet 40.

Answers
1. Greek, *akrobates*, someone who walks on tiptoe; Latin, *custos*, a guard; Greek, *deinos + saurus*, a fearful lizard; French, *espionner*, to spy; French, *gâteau*, cake; Middle English, *on grufe*, lying on your belly; Latin, *impactus*, pushed against; English, *kid + nap*; child stealing (in the 17th century, children were kidnapped to work on American plantations); Latin, *monstrum*, omen or warning; Latin, *pro + cedere*, to go onward; Latin, *super + sonus*, above sound; American Indian, *wikwam*, their house
2. Check that the children's sentences use their chosen words correctly.

Vocabulary extension

Activity 42 — Using powerful language (1)

Learning objective: *to use alternative words and expressions which are more accurate or interesting than the common choices*

Before you start
- Discuss what makes a story exciting.

- Remind the children of the word banks they built up on activity sheet 38 and look at more overused words such as *nasty*. Use the dictionary to find alternative words and start a class word bank.

- Remind children that when they edit writing to make their writing more exciting and interesting they can change words by using interesting and exciting synonyms, add or take away words, add phrases, alter the order of words or sentences, and link sentences.

Answers

1.–2. The activities will develop in a variety of ways and there are no right or wrong answers.   1. Check that the children's alternative words are acceptable. 2. Check that the children's rewritten description makes sense and uses the suggestions given.

More to do
- When the children have completed the activity discuss the vocabulary chosen. Choose some good examples to add to the word bank.

Activity 43 — Using powerful language (2)

Learning objective: *to extend common vocabulary for ways of introducing and concluding dialogue: revision and extension*

Before you start
- Remind the children that dialogue is a conversation between people and that the word *said* is often overused. It can be replaced by other words which tell the reader more about the way in which something was said.

- Ask for suggestions to put on the board.

Answers

1. groaned; whispered; announced; suggested; laughed; stuttered
2. Check that the children's rewritten dialogue makes sense.

More to do
- Look at the children's suggestions of words to replace *said* and build up a class word bank.

Creating exciting texts

Learning objective: to develop use of settings in own writing, making use of work on adjectives and figurative language to describe settings effectively

 Before you start

- Talk about how writers entice their readers into a story.

- Find some story starters. Write them on the flip chart, white board or blackboard. Discuss how they could be improved.

- Talk about drafting work. Make it clear that writers do not produce a finished piece the first time around.

- Encourage the children to proofread their own work, using a dictionary.

 More to do

- Share extracts with each other. The children can share their ideas and help each other with drafting and redrafting their material.

Creating interesting texts

Learning objective: to write a non-chronological report, including some of the organizational devices

 Before you start

- Talk about writing factual information in an interesting way. Look up some definitions from the list of words below and discuss which could be linked together and how this could be done. Remind the children how to organize their sentences into paragraphs. It is important for the children to read and understand the facts but then to reproduce them in their own words.

- There are double page spreads about the solar system and the constellations in the topic pages at the back of the *Collins Primary Dictionary*.

 Answers

There are no set answers, but the children should try to order the information in their reports logically, using connectives.

More to do

- Display the completed work alongside the drafts as part of a demonstration of dictionary use.

- Encourage further writing about outer space. Here are some headwords from the main body of the dictionary that are connected with outer space: astronaut, astronomy, constellation, eclipse, galaxy, meteor, meteorite, moon, orbit, outer space, planet, rocket, satellite, shooting star, solar system, space, spacecraft, spaceship, spacesuit, star, sun.

Name _____

What is a dictionary?

A **dictionary** is a reference book in which words are
listed alphabetically and their meanings explained.
It also tells you what part of speech a word is
and it helps you check spellings.

1. Name three other types of reference books that are arranged alphabetically.

    _____   _____   _____

2. To use a dictionary, you need to know the alphabet. Write it here from A to Z.

    _____

3. Now check this list. Write down the letters that are missing.

    a b d e f g i j k l m n o p r s t v w y z

    _____

4. Put the letters in each of these groups into alphabetical order.

    b h e k _____   h d a k _____   b a p e _____

    m w o p _____   n o l a _____   n a q p _____

5. Write down the first word and the last word in the A–Z section of your
    dictionary.

    First word: _____   Last word: _____

6. Write down the first word in the A–Z section of your dictionary that starts
    with each of these letters.

    g _____   p _____   e _____

    i _____   t _____   m _____

7. Write down the last word in the A–Z section of your dictionary that starts
    with each of these letters.

    k _____   w _____   l _____

    r _____   q _____   b _____

Using a dictionary

You can find words quickly in a dictionary because they are ordered alphabetically. You can check spellings, find the definition of a word, and find out what part of speech it is.

1. How quickly can you find words? Have a competition with a friend. Take it in turns to time each other finding each of these words.

   gift   gargoyle   coupon   stag   venom

2. Check these spellings in the dictionary. Correctly write out any word that is misspelt.

   beleeve   restaurant   peopole   mirrer   statue

   _____   _____   _____   _____   _____

3. Read the definition for *diary* and then write it in your own words.

   _____

4. Write down what part of speech each of these words is.

   image _____   sew _____   frizzy _____

   quite _____   he _____   around _____

5. What is an antonym? _____

6. Where can you find information about the spelling of difficult words, words to describe time and words for numeracy?

   _____

Revision of first and second place letters

To arrange words in alphabetical order, you look at the first letters in the words. If the first letters are the same you have to look at the second letters.

1. Sort each group of words into alphabetical order.

    checkout   severe   insect   evil   quarter   mound   laundry

    _____

    draught   wooden   antelope   tractor   unique   nice   orange

    _____

    value   yellow   balloon   reason   hurricane   plastic   fragment

    _____

2. Sort each group of words into alphabetical order looking at the *second* letter.

    crack   current   conservatory   Christmas   caveman   clinic

    _____

    special   secret   squash   saucer   scramble   sorcerer

    _____

    petal   precious   pleasant   pincers   policy   physics

    _____

3. Use your dictionary to find six examples of verbs that all begin with **d**.

    _____   _____   _____   _____   _____   _____

4. Use your dictionary to find six examples of adjectives that all begin with **r**.

    _____   _____   _____   _____   _____   _____

Third place letter

Some words have the same first and second letter.

1. Sort these words into alphabetical order looking carefully at the *third* letters.

adopt   admission   adapt   advice   adequate

_____

dimple   dive   dirty   dial   disk

_____

snow   snuggle   snap   snivel   sneak

_____

larva   lagoon   land   laboratory   late

_____

2. Write the word that follows each of these words in your dictionary.

faithful _____   everywhere _____   pottery _____

garment _____   deduct _____   trivial _____

3. Write the word that comes before each of these words in your dictionary.

_____ thud   _____ home   _____ direct

_____ see   _____ who   _____ vocal

4. Circle the word in each pair that comes first in the dictionary.

telly/temper   rhinoceros/rhubarb

sherry/shine   flock/flaunt

transport/tremble   ditch/diagonal

Name _____

Fourth place letter

Look carefully at these lists of words. Each group has the same first three letters so you will need to look at the fourth letter to put them in alphabetical order.

1. Sort these groups of words into alphabetical order according to the fourth letter.

discount	dissolve	dishonest	disregard	display

_____

notorious	notebook	nothing	noticeable

_____

speckled	speak	spend	spell	speechless

_____

wherever	when	wheat	whether	wheelbarrow

_____

2. Find four different words which begin with the same three letters below but which have a different fourth letter.

pro _____ _____ _____ _____

inf _____ _____ _____ _____

str _____ _____ _____ _____

gla _____ _____ _____ _____

3. Write the words that come before and after each of these words in your dictionary.

_____ famous _____   _____ currant _____

_____ wharf _____   _____ bulb _____

_____ vandal _____   _____ idle _____

Name _____

The four quartiles

When you open your dictionary, it helps to open it near to the word you are looking for. The four sections of the dictionary are known as the four quartiles. The sections are **a–e**, **f–m**, **n–r** and **s–z**.

1. Sort the following words into the correct quartile column in the table.

clean	weld	savings	balloon	disturb	imitate
ox	meridian	trout	projector	June	quarrel

a–e	f–m	n–r	s–z

Then sort the words from the table into alphabetical order.

_____

_____

2. Write under each of these words which quartile it fits into.

grab   never   verb   swim   roller-skate   fiend   imam   dance

____   ____   ____   ____   ____   ____   ____   ____

Write how many of these words fit in each quartile.

a–e   f–m   n–r   s–z

____   ____   ____   ____

Now write the words in alphabetical order.

_____

_____

Headwords

The words that you look up are printed in bold letters like this: **calculate**.
These words are called **headwords**. After each headword, printed in smaller
letters, there are other **forms** of the headword that can be used.

1. Write the correct form of the following headwords in
   the gap in each of these sentences. Use the dictionary
   to check for the correct form.

monster   There were three huge _____ in the clearing.

prompt   I could not think of an answer until Julie _____ me.

tackle   He was hopeless at _____ and the opposition
scored the goal.

shaky   The bridge was the _____ bridge I'd ever walked on.

litter   Rubbish _____ the streets after the storm.

flan   I made two cheese _____ for tea.

fox   The two _____ ran away from the hens when the
farmer came out.

get   She was late _____ to the bus stop but fortunately
she didn't miss the bus.

ooze   The mud _____ between my toes.

scratch   There were some _____ on the table.

grow   The trees had _____ so densely that the wood
was very dark.

The word in capitals just before each definition tells you what **part of speech**
the headword is. It might be a noun, an adjective, a verb, an adverb, a pronoun,
a preposition or a conjunction.

2. Look up each of the following words and identify what part of speech it is.

carve _____   mansion _____   royal _____

and _____   we _____   perhaps _____

across _____   friendly _____   too _____

Name _____

Guide words

The words that appear at the top of each page are called **guide words**.
The guide word on the left-hand page is the first word on that page.
The guide word on the right-hand page is the last word on that page.

1. Write the two guide words that each word in the table can be found between.

Left-hand guide word	Headword	Right-hand guide word
	carrot	
	deliberate	
	investigation	
	uncle	
	rag	
	like	
	orchid	
	right	
	swat	

2. Look up the following words, using the guide words to help you, and write a definition for each in your own words.

ridge _____

tuba _____

oats _____

limpet _____

frail _____

composer _____

Collins Primary Dictionary Skills © HarperCollinsPublishers 2001

Using the topic pages

The topic pages are at the back of the dictionary after the last entry for z.
Here is a quiz to help you find your way around them

1. What ocean lies between North America and Africa? _____

2. Is Orion in the northern or southern hemisphere? _____

3. Complete this tricky word to spell: mini_____

4. What is the short form for kilometre? _____

5. What is the Roman numeral for 5? _____

6. Name two triangles. _____ _____

7. Which planet in the solar system is nearest the sun? _____

   Which planet in the solar system is furthest from the sun? _____

8. What languages do these words come from?

Words	Original language
banquet	
alligator	
zany	
ozone	
human	
juggernaut	

Collins Primary Dictionary Skills   © HarperCollinsPublishers 2001

Name _____

Abbreviations and numbers

An abbreviation is a short form of a word. For example, *Dr* stands for *Doctor*. An abbreviation can also be made up of the first letter of a series of words, such as *EU* for *European Union*.

1. Use the Abbreviations page at the front of the dictionary to find out what these abbreviations stand for.

PTO _____

TV _____

ml _____

DVD _____

anon. _____

Use the topic pages at the back of the dictionary to find out about numbers.

2. Write the following numbers as Roman numerals.

150 _____   62 _____   8 _____   89 _____   167 _____   2004 _____

3. Write the numbers these Roman numerals stand for.

II _____   IX _____   CLIX _____   VI _____   D _____   IV _____

4. Draw a line to join each word to its definitions.

tricycle	three people singing together
biplane	a creature with one hundred feet
solo	an aeroplane with two pairs of wings
twins	an animal from mythology with one horn
duel	a three wheeled cycle
unicorn	two babies born at the same time
century	someone who is eighty years old
octogenarian	a period of one hundred years
centipede	one person singing
trio	a fight between two people

Collins Primary Dictionary Skills © HarperCollinsPublishers 2001

Name _____

Words for numeracy

Use the topic pages at the back of the dictionary to help you with these questions.

1. Write these cardinal numbers in words.

   60 _____   17 _____   42 _____

   90 _____   106 _____

   1 000 _____   10 002 _____

   10 100 _____   1 000 000 _____

2. Write the words for these ordinal numbers.

   8th _____   1st _____   21st _____

   3rd _____   20th _____   15th _____

3. Name these shapes.

   _____   _____   _____

4. Use the A–Z section of the dictionary to help you find these words.

   What do these numeracy words mean?

   digit _____

   less _____

   diagonal _____

   circumference _____

   axis _____

   matrix _____

   per cent _____

   quotient _____

   right angle _____

Name _____

Prefixes and suffixes

A **prefix** is added to the **beginning** of a word to change its meaning. When a prefix is added to a word it does not change the spelling of the root word.

These are some common prefixes.

> **super- il- in- re- un- non- dis- post- co-**

1. Add an ending to each of these prefixes to make a word that fits the definition. Then check your answers in the dictionary.

   under_____ : below the surface of the ground

   mis_____ : not being able to trust someone

   sub_____ : to go or push something beneath the surface of a liquid

   re_____ : to be seen again after something has been out of sight

   pre_____ : existing at a time in the past before anything was written down

   tele_____ : a piece of electrical equipment for talking to someone who is at a distance

A **suffix** is added to the **end** of a word to change its meaning.
A suffix can change the **tense** of a verb:

> walk (present tense) → walk**ed** (past tense).

It can change the **class** of a word:

> walk (verb) → walk**er** (noun).

2. Choose one of these suffixes to add to each of the following words.

> **-er -est -able -ant -dom -ly -hood -ness**
> **-less -ous -ful -ist -ic -ing -ed**

Sometimes the spelling of the root word changes when you add a suffix, so use your dictionary to check the spelling.

swim_____   help_____   child_____   snap_____

king_____   crack_____   sad_____   truth_____

art_____   danger_____   attend_____   light_____

Synonyms and antonyms

Synonyms are words with similar meanings.

join   link   tie

1. Find a synonym for each underlined word.

   Why don't we <u>join</u> the ropes together so they reach
   across the stream?   _____

   The <u>motor</u> in the machine stopped running.   _____

   You will have to <u>prove</u> that what you say is true.   _____

   My little sister is <u>wilful</u> and never does what she is told. _____

   He was <u>very</u> happy with his present.   _____

Antonyms are words that have opposite meanings.
Antonyms are often formed by adding prefixes to root words.

2. Find an antonym for each underlined word and rewrite the sentence
   so it makes sense.

   The <u>digital</u> watch was easy to read as the time was shown in numbers.

   _____

   The party was very <u>formal</u> and everyone was wearing smart clothes.

   _____

   It was <u>dark</u> so I could not see the hole in front of me and I fell down it!

   _____

   You were <u>right</u> on all your answers so you can have a team point.

   _____

   There is <u>less</u> time than I thought so we will have to hurry.

   _____

Asking questions

A **question** usually begins with the question words *who, whose, what, why, when, where, which* or *how*.

1. These are the answers to some questions. Can you work out what the question was and write it down?

   Play was cancelled because it rained.

   _____

   The ball was stuck on the garage roof.

   _____

   It was him, Miss!

   _____

   Michelle has the longest hair in the class.

   _____

   I'm doing my homework.

   _____

   First, you switch on the computer. Then you click on the start icon. After that you choose which programme you want to run and click on that.

   _____

2. This is a statement: *The weeds were growing in Mr Jones' window box.*
   Find five ways to turn this statement into a question using some of the question words above.

   1. _____

   2. _____

   3. _____

   4. _____

   5. _____

Activity 15

Name _____

Prepositions (1)

A **preposition** is a word that links two nouns or pronouns.
A preposition tells us the **position** of one thing in relation to another.
Prepositions often tell you about place, movement or time.

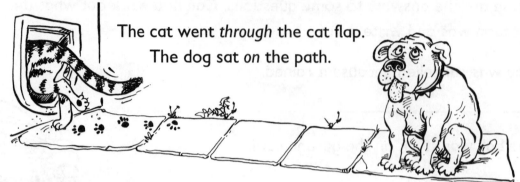

The cat went *through* the cat flap.
The dog sat *on* the path.

Here are some common prepositions.

> **about   above   across   against   along   amid   around   at**
> **behind   below   beneath   beside   between   beyond   by   down**
> **except   for   from   in   inside   like   near   of   off   over   since**
> **through   till   to   towards   under   until   up   upon   with**

Choose prepositions to link the nouns and verbs in these sentences.

They rode _____ the bridge on their bikes.

The postman avoids the dog at Number 6 by putting the

letters _____ the hedge.

They sheltered from the rain _____ the umbrella.

The builder leaned the ladder _____ the wall.

They watched the badgers all night _____ dawn.

The kittens slept in a box _____ the fire.

Her seat on the train was _____ the buffet car.

The nurse wrapped the bandage _____ Andy's knee.

Marie had not seen her friend _____ several days.

A vase of flowers had been placed _____ the table.

They put their homework _____ the teacher's tray.

He placed a bookmark _____ the pages.

Name _____

Prepositions (2)

Here is a piece of text with all the prepositions missing.
Can you fill in the missing words?

As they walked _____ the woods it began to get dark.

It was cold now and they wished they had not set out so late.

They could feel that there was something or someone following

close _____ them so they wanted to find shelter as soon

as they could. It was not long _____ they saw a gate

and they ran _____ it. It was padlocked, and now they

could hear the sound of footsteps coming _____ the

path. They were terrified. The gate was _____ them

and safety. There was nothing for it but to climb _____

or crawl _____ the gate. They scrambled _____

brambles and nettles then launched themselves at the gate.

Not a moment too soon they found themselves _____

the gate. They had landed _____ a heap in the

mud, but at least they were safe.

 Collins Primary Dictionary Skills © HarperCollinsPublishers 2001

Nouns and verbs

A **noun** is a **naming word**. Nouns can be
singular (just one) or **plural** (more than one).

1. Write the plural of each of these nouns
   then check your spellings in the dictionary.

   potato _____   army _____   goose _____

   piano _____   valley _____   wolf _____

   woman _____   roof _____   child _____

Capital letters are used to **start sentences**,
to **begin proper nouns** and to write the word *I*.

2. Put the capital letters into the following passage.

   the *brittania* was due to dock in bristol at noon. hundreds of people had

   gathered to see her sail up the river avon. they had banners and flags

   to welcome her. it was a bright day, although a little cloudy. suddenly,

   a murmur ran through the crowd. a dark shape began to form in

   the distance. soon they could see the ship with the crew lined up to

   wave back at them. madge, ida and i cheered along with the rest.

Verbs are **action words**. They have past, present and future tenses.

3. Put the correct form of the verb into the space in each sentence.

   They _____ yesterday.   (argued/argue/will argue)

   I hope my horse _____ the race tomorrow.   (will win/winning/won)

   She had _____ for a walk.   (go/gone/went)

   The old man _____ asleep in his chair.   (fell/fallen/falling)

   The boy was _____ about football.   (dreamed/dreaming/dreamt)

Adjectives and adverbs

Adjectives are **describing words**. They tell us more about nouns or pronouns.

1. Underline the adjectives in these sentences.

   The tall boy wore huge shoes.

   The pink flower had delicate petals.

   The weather was hot and humid.

   We found the lost ball by the old gate.

   There were seven boys and three girls in the team.

Adverbs tell us more about verbs.

2. Underline the adverbs in these sentences.

   Tea will soon be ready.

   She listened anxiously to the news.

   The dog trembled terribly when she heard a clap of thunder.

   They slept soundly after the long walk.

   He walked slowly towards the open door.

3. Add some adjectives and adverbs to these sentences to make them more interesting.

   The cat crept _____ into the _____ grass and

   slept _____.

   He waited _____ beside the _____ tree in case the foxes came by.

   The river flows _____ under the _____ bridge.

   The _____ teacher frowned _____ at the _____ children.

   The _____ stranger knocked _____ on the _____ door.

Connectives

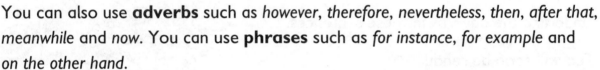

Conjunctions are words that **connect** parts of a sentence.

1. Underline the conjunctions in these sentences.

   The dog ran until he caught up with the postman's bike.

   The boy waved whenever he saw his sister.

   I ate breakfast before I went to school.

   He left as darkness was falling.

   He read a book while I wrote the note.

   We knew whose fault it was because we saw it happen.

   He was not famous in Australia although he had starred in a film there.

You can also use **adverbs** such as *however, therefore, nevertheless, then, after that, meanwhile* and *now*. You can use **phrases** such as *for instance, for example* and *on the other hand*.

2. Use one or more connectives to join each pair of sentences.

   The woman finished her sandwich. She got on the train.

   _____

   He could not afford the picture. He wanted to buy it.

   _____

   Your drawing has improved. You have these new pencils.

   _____

   Some of the paper was coloured. There were red and blue sheets.

   _____

   They worked hard in the garden. Mum made them some sandwiches.

   _____

   I would like to go to the park. I would like to watch a film, too.

   _____

More than one meaning

Some words have more than one meaning or can be used in several different ways.

1. Look up these words. Write the number of meanings given for each word.

hoard ____   mangle ____   tackle ____   will ____

Now choose one meaning of each word and write a sentence using it to show that you understand the meaning. The first one has been done for you.

hoard   <u>The dragon sleeps on his hoard of golden treasure under the mountain.</u>

mangle   _____

tackle   _____

will   _____

2. Write two sentences for each of the words below to show two different meanings of each word.
For example, *complex* can mean a group of buildings.
It can also mean something that is difficult to understand:

   I was lost in the sports <u>complex</u> for three hours.
   I can't do this puzzle. It's too <u>complex</u> for me.

rumble   _____

_____

narrow   _____

_____

present   _____

_____

font   _____

_____

Writing definitions

A **definition** helps a reader to understand the **meaning** of the word. Sometimes it is necessary to give an example sentence to show how the word is used.

Look up each of the following words in your dictionary. Then, using your own words, write a definition for each of them.

assorted (adjective)

Definition: _____

permission (noun)

Definition: _____

letter (noun)

Definition 1: _____

letter (noun)

Definition 2: _____

guard (verb)

Definition 1: _____

guard (noun)

Definition 2: _____

grumpy (adjective)

Definition: _____

dinosaur (noun)

Definition: _____

comic (noun)

Definition 1: _____

comic (adjective)

Definition 2: _____

charcoal (noun)

Definition: _____

Collins Primary Dictionary Skills © HarperCollinsPublishers 2001

Defining words

Choose one of these lists of words and make up a clue about each word in the list using your dictionary to help you. Write your clues down in any order and swap your list of clues with a friend. Work out which word is the answer to each clue.

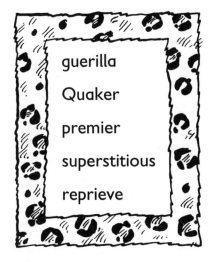

guerilla

Quaker

premier

superstitious

reprieve

sachet

onomatopoeia

fen

fluid

outspoken

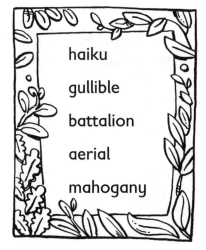

haiku

gullible

battalion

aerial

mahogany

outrage

symmetry

ascend

cliffhanger

truant

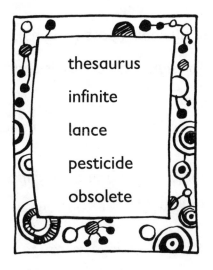

thesaurus

infinite

lance

pesticide

obsolete

Talmud

carbohydrate

juggernaut

tamper

nostalgia

flammable

acknowledge

eminent

ruthless

coward

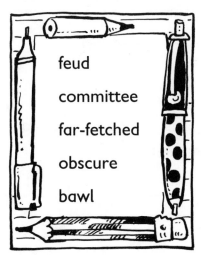

feud

committee

far-fetched

obscure

bawl

brochure

deflate

quarantine

incident

aviary

Related words

When you look a word up in a dictionary, make a point of noticing related words listed before and after it. These words can make up a word family. For example, if you look up *reality*, you will find the related words *real* and *realistic* before it and *realize* and *really* after it.

1. Look for related words for the following. Remember the words must have something in common in their meaning.

    cave _____

    micro _____

    ice _____

    detect _____

    pacify _____

Sometimes words are related by their roots (origins).

Signum is the Latin word for *sign*. These words share the root word *sign*:

sign   *signal*   *signature*   *signify*   *resign*   *design*

2. What do you think the words *magnify* and *magnificent* have in common in their meanings?

    magnify means: _____

    magnificent means: _____

    common meaning: _____

3. What do you think the words *pedal* and *pedestrian* have in common in their meanings?

    pedal means: _____

    pedestrian means: _____

    common meaning: _____

Root words

A **root word** is the word (or part of the word) you are left with when you take away any prefixes or suffixes.

unexpectedly = un + **expect** + ed + ly
The root word is *expect*. The prefix is *un-* and the suffixes are *-ed* and *-ly*.

1. Divide these words into prefix, root word and suffix. Sometimes the spelling of the root word has to change. The first one has been done for you.

	Prefix	**Root word**	**Suffix**
disobedient	dis-	obey	-ient
dissatisfied			
underestimated			
unlikely			
prematurely			
irresistible			

2. Add a prefix, suffix or both to make new words from each of these these root words. Sometimes the spelling of the root words changes. The first one has been done for you.

write   <u>writer</u>   <u>writing</u>   <u>written</u>   <u>unwritten</u>

accept   _____

regard   _____

claim   _____

rely   _____

control   _____

believe   _____

Name _____

Word building

Compound words are made from two smaller words put together.

table + *cloth* = *tablecloth*   *egg* + *cup* = *eggcup*   *tea* + *pot* = *teapot*

1. Think of another word to add to the following to make a compound word.

    _____ache   post_____   snow_____   _____ground

    _____light   life_____   _____drop   moon_____

    _____noon   foot_____   _____board

Nouns can be formed from other parts of speech.

2. Form nouns from these words. Use your dictionary to help you.

    wealthy (adjective) ___wealth___   think (verb)   _____

    imagine (verb)   _____   see (verb)   _____

    operate (verb)   _____   attract (verb)   _____

    cruel (adjective)   _____   collect (verb)   _____

    friendly (adjective) _____   breathless (adjective) _____

Adjectives can be formed from nouns.

3. Form adjectives from these nouns.

    child ___childish___   five _____   silk _____

    storm _____   favour _____   care _____

    danger _____   peace _____   sun _____

Adverbs can be formed from other parts of speech.

4. Form adverbs from these words.

    happy (adjective) ___happily___   true (adjective) _____

    horror (noun)   _____   sweet (adjective) _____

    heavy (adjective) _____   noise (noun)   _____

Homophones

Homophones are words that **sound the same** but have **different spellings and meanings**.

1. Underline the correct word for the picture. Use your dictionary to help you.

boy/buoy

key/quay

whale/wail

dough/doe

ruff/rough

sure/shore

2. Write a short sentence for each of these words to show its correct use.

coarse _____

course _____

mane _____

main _____

heard _____

herd _____

3. Underline the right word.

My friend was bored/board with the lesson and fell asleep.

She acted as the principal/principle boy
in the pantomime.

They will higher/hire a car for the holiday in Spain.

My sister let out a groan/grown as she twisted her ankle.

There/Their books were lying on the floor/flaw.

The shrine was a holy/wholly place/plaice.

The house that was for sail/sale was too dear/deer for them to by/buy.

Silent letters

Some words have letters in them that you cannot hear when the word is spoken.

1. Put a ring around the silent letters in these words.

fasten	debt	gnome	shepherd
ghost	hours	wriggle	lambs
knelt	condemn	light	autumn
muscles	descend	comb	night

2. Here are some clues to words that have silent letters.
   Write the words then check the spelling in the dictionary.

   This number comes after seventeen.   _____

   This pipe carries fumes out of a vehicle's engine.   _____

   You use a pair of these to cut out paper.   _____

   This is a regular beat in music or poetry.   _____

   This day comes after Tuesday.   _____

3. Write these words in the correct columns.

wreck	bomb	wrap	knight
write	doubt	knot	sword
knit	crumb	knee	climb

silent **b**	silent **k**	silent **w**

Spelling tricky words

Some words are not easy to spell and you need to pay special attention to them.
Proofread the following story and correct any misspellings. There are 17!
Write the correct spelling above the word. Use your dictionary to help you.

A far-fetched tale

"My jewelry, my jewellery! My beautiful necklace!" she screamed. "It's a

cattastrofy! Where was the security gard?" She sat down in dispare and wept.

When he arrived, the security garde was embarast. "I was argueing with a

naybor. I told him to get rid of that box of tomatos he left by the libry.

Don't worry, it will be fine."

She began to have all sorts of imaginerry ideas.

Perhaps the gardner had taken it. He had looked

very misterious earlier. Or maybe a baloon had

brought in a stranger. Even someone

in camerflage could have crept in

unseen and seezed it.

Suddenly she felt redickulus. She caught

sight of herself in the mirror and

there it was, round her neck!

When to use apostrophes

When you are confused over words that sound alike, learn them separately. Learn them by their meaning or by the way they look.

its whose there their your	it's who's they're you're he's she's

Words that are joined and shortened (contractions) have an apostrophe in the place of the missing letter: **Who's** is the contraction for who is; **they're** is the contraction for they are.

Who's coming to the party? They're all coming!

1. Complete these sentences using words from the correct box above.

_____ very happy with her present.

_____ so kind of you to ask me to tea.

_____ not all telling you the truth.

The words **their** and **there** are easily confused. **Their** always means 'belonging to them'. It is a possessive word. Their is the plural of his, her and its. **There** can be used in two ways. It can be used to show a place where something is happening. It can also be used in sayings like "there is" and "there are".

2. Proofread this paragraph and choose the correct word from each bracket, checking in your dictionary to help you. Underline each correct word.

Jo and I are going to the swimming pool with the Greens.

(There / Their / They're) taking us (there / their / they're) in

(there / their/ they're) car. I'm looking forward to the water splash,

as (its / it's) always exciting. (Theres / Theirs / There's) a diving

board too. We'll have ice cream after our swim. My favourite is

choc-mint because (its / it's) really creamy. Jo's favourite is

strawberry. (Hes / He's) eaten four at once for a dare!

Name _____

Patterns in spelling

These words have the same **letter string** (*ough*) but **different pronunciations**.

r**ough** (pronounced *ruff*)   c**ough** (pronounced *coff*)
tr**ough** (rhymes with *off*)   pl**ough** (rhymes with *cow*)
d**ough** (rhymes with *blow*)   thr**ough** (pronounced *threw*)

1. Underline the common letter string in each group. Circle the odd word out
   that has a different pronunciation.

goose	loose	choose	moose		sour	route	south	mouse
dove	move	love	glove		hear	heard	beard	dear
work	cork	pork	stork		lead	dead	bead	tread
meat	great	treat	cheat		eight	height	weight	freight

2. Write a sentence using both the words in each group to help you
   to remember the spelling pattern. One has been done for you.

card   ward

I took a get-well **card** to my mum who was in Daffodil **ward**.

hours   four

_____

guide   bruise

_____

find   windmill

_____

cloth   both

_____

glow   flower

_____

Irregular verbs

Some verb forms do not follow the usual patterns of spelling when you form different tenses.

Verb	Forms							
To be	am	are	is	be	being	been	was	were
To come	come	comes	coming	came				
To do	do	does	doing	did	done			
To go	go	goes	going	went	gone			
To have	have	has	having	had				

1. Choose the correct word from the table to complete these sentences.

   Are you _____ with us to the party? She _____ five minutes ago.

   I _____ hungry now. What shall we _____ first?

   We _____ behaving ourselves and we are _____ a good time.

   He _____ look funny! He is _____ some good tricks.

   Are you _____ careful with those plates?

2. Write the correct form for the past tense of the verb in these sentences.

   The boys _____ they had a successful match. (to say)

   I _____ a bar of chocolate this morning. (to eat)

   You _____ about the test yesterday, didn't you? (to know)

   They _____ a wonderful picnic. (to bring)

   They _____ not to join in. (to choose)

   I _____ a letter to my Gran. (to write)

   It was so cold that the ground was _____. (to freeze)

   The dog _____ barking all night. (to keep)

Name _____

Rhyming games

When two words **rhyme**, both words have a very **similar sound**.
Some pairs of rhyming words have the same letter string or spelling pattern.

ape/grape   **half/calf**   **arm/charm**

1. Find some rhymes with the same spelling pattern as each of these words.

   band _____ _____ _____ _____

   chip _____ _____ _____ _____

   late _____ _____ _____ _____

   stake _____ _____ _____ _____

Some pairs of rhyming words do not have the same spelling pattern.

cough / off   plough / bow   real / feel

2. Find some rhymes with a different spelling pattern from each of these words.

   lawn _____ _____ _____ _____

   hair _____ _____ _____ _____

   paw _____ _____ _____ _____

3. Think of a rhyming word which will make sense to complete the line.

   When I was small, my teddy bear

   Would sit upon a big arm_____

   And from the fruit bowl we would share

   A lovely, shiny, juicy _____ .

   He would always laugh and laugh

   When I cut the pear in _____ .

Name _____

Word search (1)

There are 12 tricky words to spell hidden in this letter square. Can you find them?

Y	R	P	M	X	J	E	A	L	O	U	S
H	I	C	C	U	P	X	D	M	P	P	B
T	D	I	E	S	E	L	E	T	F	E	A
L	I	B	R	A	R	Y	V	W	M	O	L
W	C	X	V	C	K	I	E	E	O	P	L
L	U	R	P	A	R	A	L	L	E	L	O
B	L	C	D	E	S	T	O	F	E	E	O
N	O	Q	W	G	H	I	P	T	B	F	N
Q	U	I	E	T	A	J	O	H	O	D	O
A	S	B	E	A	U	T	I	F	U	L	C

Encircle each word as you find it and write the words here.

b_____   b_____   d_____

d_____   h_____   j_____

l_____   p_____   p_____

q_____   r_____   t_____

Name _____

Word search (2)

There are 12 words to do with time hidden in this
letter square. Can you find them?

Y	F	R	E	Q	U	E	N	T	L	Y
D	E	E	B	R	D	E	S	O	O	N
U	L	I	S	A	K	L	U	N	P	Q
R	A	S	P	R	I	N	G	Q	U	R
A	P	G	A	E	W	N	E	V	E	R
T	S	H	N	L	W	X	P	T	U	E
I	E	V	I	Y	Y	C	A	E	O	N
O	I	M	M	E	M	O	R	I	A	L
N	T	W	I	C	E	P	Y	T	H	S
M	J	E	T	E	R	N	I	T	Y	F

Encircle each word as you find it and write the words here.

a_____ d_____ e_____ e_____

f_____ i_____ n_____ r_____

s_____ s_____ s_____ t_____

Name _____

Crossword (1)

Remember to check your spellings in your dictionary.

Across

1. Jump lightly from one foot to the other over a rope
3. The fifth month
4. A work of art made by shaping stone, clay or wood
5. A large hole in a cliff or under the ground
6. Unkind
8. Nettles or bees can do this to you

Down

2. The state of being ill
3. A light purple colour
4. Something you wear on your foot to keep it warm
7. The opposite of yes

Name _____

Crossword (2)

Check your spellings
in your dictionary.

Across

1. A town representative.

4. Short for "for example".

5. A French cook

7. You can watch TV __ __ you do your homework first.

8. A long thin fish.

9. Hair that is this is very wiry and curly.

Down

1. Something you can get into when you are naughty.

2. Sing in the Alps!

3. This colour traffic light makes you stop.

6. A race where several members of a team take turns.

Name _____

New words

onomatopoeia photosynthesis ricochet

Find six words from your reading book, or other books you are using in class, that you would not normally use in your own writing. Write them here. Look up their meanings in the dictionary and write each definition in your own words. Then make up a sentence using the word to show its meaning.

1. _____

Definition: _____

Sentence: _____

2. _____

Definition: _____

Sentence: _____

3. _____

Definition: _____

Sentence: _____

4. _____

Definition: _____

Sentence: _____

5. _____

Definition: _____

Sentence: _____

6. _____

Definition: _____

Sentence: _____

Overused words

Some words are used so often that they no longer
have much meaning or they are boring.

then nice & got then good got the good got nice good nice nice then got nice then got

1. Gather some synonyms for each word shown at the top of the
    following columns so that you can make your written work more interesting.

good	got	nice	then

Now write a sentence using one of the synonyms from each column.

a) _____

b) _____

c) _____

d) _____

2. Find synonyms for the words in these columns.

speak	walk	drink	eat

Now write a sentence using one of the synonyms from each column.

a) _____

b) _____

c) _____

d) _____

Collins Primary Dictionary Skills © HarperCollinsPublishers 2001

Name _____

Topic-based word banks

1. These words are to do with the **environment**.
   What do they mean? Use your dictionary to help you.

   ecology

   Definition: _____

   greenhouse effect

   Definition: _____

   ozone layer

   Definition: _____

   conservation

   Definition: _____

   atmosphere

   Definition: _____

2. These are words to do with **energy**. What do they mean? Use your
   dictionary to help you.

   solar

   Definition: _____

   hydroelectric

   Definition: _____

   microwave

   Definition: _____

   turbine

   Definition: _____

   generator

   Definition: _____

Etymology (1)

Our language is very exciting as it has many words from other languages
and peoples.

1. Use the "Words from other languages" list in your dictionary and write down
   which language each of the words below came from.

   benefit _____   bungalow _____   tapestry _____

   thug   _____   autograph _____   daisy   _____

   hour   _____   observe   _____

2. Use your dictionary to help you fill in the gaps. Find out which language
   each underlined word comes from and what it meant originally.

   Example: The word _colossal_ comes from the Greek word
   kolossus meaning a large statue.

   The word _manual_ comes from the _____

   word _____ meaning _____ .

   The word _Tuesday_ comes from A_____ and

   this day honoured the god of _____ , T_____ .

   The word _pyjamas_ comes from the _____ language

   and it meant _____ .

   The word _rendezvous_ comes from _____ and meant _____

   _____ .

   The word _lollipop_ comes from _____ . _Lolli_ meant _____

   and _____ meant apple. Originally _lollipop_ meant a red apple on a stick.

3. Now choose three of the words from question 2 and write a sentence for each
   to show how the word is used today.

   a) _____

   b) _____

   c) _____

Name _____

Etymology (2)

1. Look up these words in your dictionary and write down where they come from.

Word	Original language	Original word(s)	Meaning of original word
acrobat	Greek	akrobates	someone who walks on tiptoe
custody			
dinosaur			
espionage			
gateau			
grovel			
impact			
kidnap			
monster			
proceed			
supersonic			
wigwam			

2. Choose four of the words that most interest you and write a sentence for each word.

a) _____

b) _____

c) _____

d) _____

Name _____

Using powerful language (1)

You can make your writing exciting and interesting by using your dictionary to help you. For example, you can improve the sentence "She was a *nasty* child." Look up *nasty* in your dictionary. The definition is "very unpleasant". There are also some synonyms: *unkind*, *rude*, *disgusting*. So there are four alternatives to *nasty* which could make your sentence more interesting and more powerful.

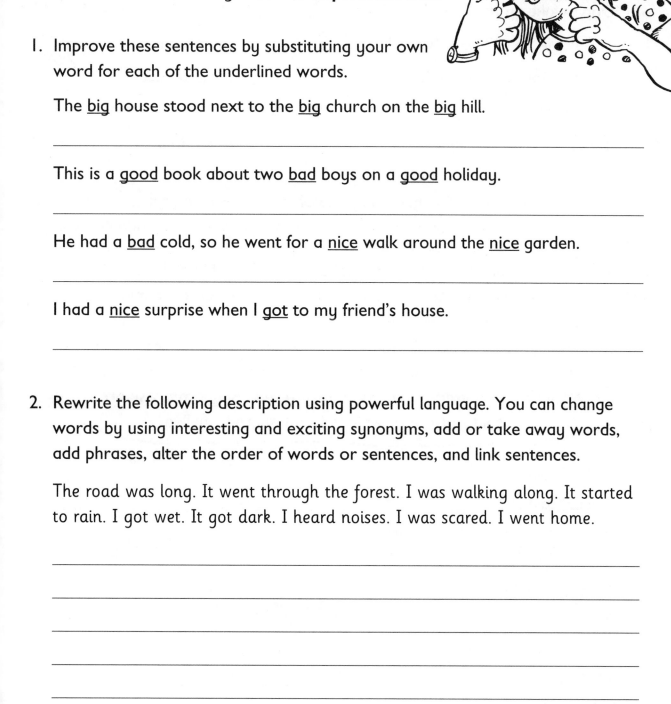

　　　　She was a very *rude* and *unpleasant* child.

1. Improve these sentences by substituting your own word for each of the underlined words.

   The <u>big</u> house stood next to the <u>big</u> church on the <u>big</u> hill.

   _____

   This is a <u>good</u> book about two <u>bad</u> boys on a <u>good</u> holiday.

   _____

   He had a <u>bad</u> cold, so he went for a <u>nice</u> walk around the <u>nice</u> garden.

   _____

   I had a <u>nice</u> surprise when I <u>got</u> to my friend's house.

   _____

2. Rewrite the following description using powerful language. You can change words by using interesting and exciting synonyms, add or take away words, add phrases, alter the order of words or sentences, and link sentences.

   The road was long. It went through the forest. I was walking along. It started to rain. I got wet. It got dark. I heard noises. I was scared. I went home.

   _____

   _____

   _____

   _____

   _____

Name _____

Using powerful language (2)

Dialogue is a **conversation** between people. The dialogue word *said* can be replaced by other words that tell the reader more about how something is said.

1. Choose the best dialogue word to complete each sentence.

whispered   groaned   stuttered   announced   suggested   laughed

"I don't feel very well," the sick child _____.

"Don't wake up the baby," Mrs Muna _____.

"This is the Ten O'clock News!" _____ the newsreader.

"Perhaps you could write it this way," _____ the teacher.

"That does look funny," _____ the twins.

"It must be a g...g...g...ghost," _____ the terrified boy.

2. Rewrite the following dialogue using one of these words to replace *said*.
   Your choice of words can make the situation seem happy, sad, funny or scary.

> announced   answered   asked   babbled   blurted   called
> claimed   commented   complained   cried   declared   demanded
> exclaimed   explained   expressed   gasped   groaned   grumbled
> hinted   insisted   laughed   mentioned   mumbled   muttered   narrated
> pointed out   promised   recited   remarked   replied   shouted
> snarled   spluttered   stressed   stuttered   suggested   swore
> told   uttered   whinged   whispered   yelled

"Hello," said Mary. _____

"Hello," said Jez. _____

"Why are you here?" said Mary. _____

"He sent for me," said Jez. _____

"Me too," said Mary. _____

The door opened. _____

"Come in," said Mr Jones. _____

"Oh," said Mary. _____

"Oh," said Jez. _____

Creating exciting texts

Read the story starter. What do you think happens next at the start of this story? Continue the story starter, making the reader want to go on. Write your first draft on spare paper, using your dictionary to help you to **check spellings** and **find alternative words** to make it exciting. Read through your first draft. You might want to make alterations or check spellings again. Use your dictionary to help you. When you have completed your second draft, write your story starter out here.

She didn't notice the two green eyes watching her from behind the window of the house next door.

_____
_____
_____
_____
_____
_____
_____
_____
_____
_____
_____
_____
_____
_____
_____
_____
_____
_____
_____

Name _____

Creating interesting texts

On a separate piece of paper, write a simple non-chronological report about outer space. Use your dictionary to find information. Make notes on this page from the information that you find out and then re-draft your notes to write a report using effective language. Remember to use connectives, vary the sentence lengths and use only the most important details.

Organize your writing into four paragraphs. Each paragraph should be about 50 words long. Here are some planning boxes to help you. Remember to use your own words.

Paragraph 1: What is the solar system?

Paragraph 2: What are the most important features of the solar system?

Paragraph 3: Write about some of the interesting features of some of the planets.

Paragraph 4: Choose one planet to write about in detail.